In Tune

JIM DAVIS

RAVETTE BOOKS

First published by
Ravette Books Limited 1991

Printed and bound in Great Britain
for Ravette Books Limited,
3 Glenside Estate, Star Road, Partridge Green,
Horsham, West Sussex RH13 8RA
by Cox & Wyman Ltd, Reading

ISBN 1 85304 331 1

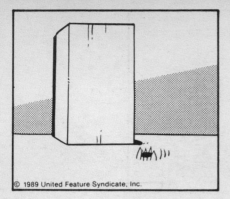

© 1989 United Feature Syndicate, Inc.

JIM DAVIS 11-20

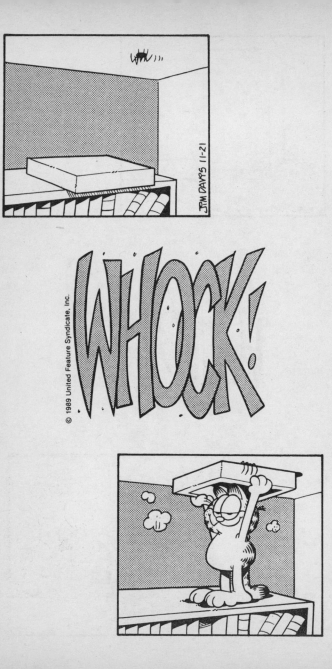

© 1989 United Feature Syndicate, Inc.

JM DAVPS

12-5

YOU'RE NOT EVEN CLOSE, GARFIELD

© 1989 United Feature Syndicate, Inc.

BOY, CAN THAT GUY HIDE A CHRISTMAS PRESENT OR WHAT?

JIM DAVIS

GARFIELD, WHAT MADE YOU DO THAT?!

© 1989 United Feature Syndicate, Inc.

I THINK IT WAS THE EARFLAPS

JPM DAVPS

© 1989 United Feature Syndicate, Inc.

HOW GOES
THE DIET?

OH...YOU
KNOW

© 1990 United Feature Syndicate, inc.

© 1990 United Feature Syndicate, Inc.

© 1990 United Feature Syndicate, Inc.

JIM DAVIS

1-22

HERE, JON!
HAVE A BONE

© 1-23

WHERE DID YOU
GET THIS?

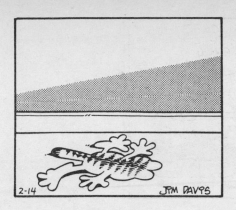

NOBODY CAN RELAX LIKE YOU, GARFIELD. HOW DO YOU DO IT?

SLIPPING WHILE SWINGING FROM THE LIGHT FIXTURE HELPS

© 1990 United Feature Syndicate, Inc.

© 1990 United Feature Syndicate, Inc.

2-16 JIM DAVIS

JIM DAVIS

2-20

© 1990 United Feature Syndicate, Inc.

GULP! ___

© 1990 United Feature Syndicate, Inc.

© 1990 United Feature Syndicate, Inc.

© 1990 United Feature Syndicate, Inc.

THANKS

FOOF

AND THE CROWD
GOES WILD

JIM DAVIS 3-10

IN CASE YOU DIDN'T NOTICE, I JUST CHASED A MOUSE THROUGH HERE!

© 1990 United Feature Syndicate, Inc.

BRAVO

CLAP CLAP CLAP

JIM DAVIS

3-12

ODIE AND I ARE GOING TO PLAY ON THE ROOF

© 1990 United Feature Syndicate, Inc.

ROLLER SKATES?!

LOOK OUT BELOW!

JIM DAVIS 3-13

© 1990 United Feature Syndicate, Inc.

© 1990 United Feature Syndicate, Inc.

© 1990 United Feature Syndicate, Inc.

© 1990 United Feature Syndicate, Inc.

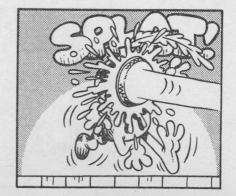

OTHER GARFIELD BOOKS IN THIS SERIES

LANDSCAPE SERIES

COLOUR TV SPECIALS

Here Comes Garfield	£2.95
Garfield On The Town	£2.95
Garfield In The Rough	£2.95
Garfield In Disguise	£2.95
Garfield In Paradise	£2.95
Garfield Goes To Hollywood	£2.95
A Garfield Christmas	£2.95
Garfield's Thanksgiving	£2.95

COLOUR TREASURIES

The Second Garfield Treasury	£5.95
The Third Garfield Treasury	£5.95
The Fourth Garfield Treasury	£5.95
The Fifth Garfield Treasury	£5.95
Garfield A Weekend Away	£4.95
Garfield Book Of Cat Names	£2.50
Garfield Best Ever	£4.95
Garfield The Easter Bunny?	£3.95
Garfield How To Party	£3.95
Garfield Selection	£5.95
Garfield His 9 Lives	£5.95

All these books are available at your local bookshop or newsagent, or can be ordered direct from the publisher. Just tick the titles you require and fill in the form below. Prices and availability subject to change without notice.

Ravette Books Limited, 3 Glenside Estate, Star Road, Partridge Green, Horsham, West Sussex RH13 8RA

Please send a cheque or postal order and allow the following for postage and packing. UK: Pocket-books – 45p for one book, 20p for a second book and 15p for each additional book. Landscape Series – 50p for one book plus 30p for each additional book. TV Specials and Cat Names – 45p for one book plus 30p for each additional book. Other titles – 85p for one book plus 50p for each additional book ordered.

Name ....

Address ....

....